Lots of things to draw

Fiona Watt, Rebecca Gilpin,
Leonie Pratt and Louie Stowell

Designed and illustrated by Stella Baggott,
Katrina Fearn, Non Figg, Erica Harrison, Katie Lovell,
Jan McCafferty, Samantha Meredith and Antonia Miller

Contents

Playful penguins

Use the ideas shown here to make a picture with penguins in the sea and on an iceberg.

For a swimming penguin, glue the beak onto the back of the head, at the top.

Draw fish on shiny paper, then cut them out and glue them on.

1. Using a blue pencil, draw an arch for a penguin's body on black paper. Add a wavy line for the bottom of the body, and a tail to one side.

2. Draw a small arch for the tummy. Add a flipper on each side of the body. Then, cut around the penguin, leaving a narrow black border.

Draw lines on the feet, too.

3. Using a dark orange pencil, draw a pointed beak on a piece of orange paper. Then, draw two feet with curves along the bottom.

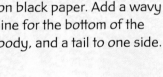

This iceberg was filled in with watery blue paint and left to dry. Then, thick white paint was brushed roughly over the top.

4. Cut out the beak and the feet. Glue the beak onto the penguin. Then, dab glue onto the feet. Press them onto the back of the body, like this.

5. Fill in a soft shape on the tummy with a white pencil. Draw small white circles for the eyes. Then, add dots on them with a black pencil.

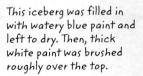

5

Delivery trucks

For a scene like this, paint a road and road signs after you've painted the trucks. Add black outlines when all the paint is dry.

1. Mix yellow paint with some water on an old plate. Then, paint a large rectangle on a piece of white paper for the truck's trailer.

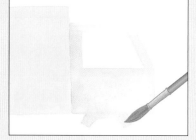

2. Mix pale blue paint with some water. Then, paint a cab at one end of the trailer. Add a curved shape at the bottom of the cab for a mudguard.

3. When all the paint is dry, paint three black wheels. Add a safety bar between the wheels, like this. Then, leave the paint to dry completely.

You could draw a
truck with an open
top and fill it with
anything you like.

PETE'S PLANTS

4. Using a thin black felt-tip pen, carefully draw around all the parts of the truck. Draw a door on the cab, then add a shape for a handle.

5. Draw a mirror on the cab, then draw a driver. Fill in the driver with felt-tip pens. Then, draw a picture on the trailer for a logo.

6. Using a thin silver pen, add circles for hubcaps. Draw dots for bolts on the wheels too. Then, fill in the mirror and the door handle.

7

Painted fairies

You could paint a whole scene with lots of fairies — look at this picture for ideas.

For a standing fairy, arrange the painted shapes differently in step 1.

Paint a big pond, then add lily pads and swimming fish.

Make the hair overlap the head a little.

Overlap the wings.

Draw a star at the end of the wand, too.

1. Paint a circle for a fairy's head on white paper, then add her hair. Paint a dress, then add two wings above it. Paint a yellow spot for a wand, too.

2. Using a thin black pen, draw the fairy's face, with a little nose and an ear. Draw her dress and two little feet. Then, add two leaf-shaped wings.

3. Draw the fairy's arms, with one arm stretching out. Add a wand, with a line above and below her hand, like this. Draw wavy lines on the hair.

Paint bright blobs for flowers, then add petals when the paint is dry.

Looking around

You can make a fairy look down or up by drawing her eyes, nose and mouth in different places on her face.

Looking down: draw the eyes in the middle, then add the nose and mouth at the bottom.

Looking up: draw a fairy's eyes and nose at the top of her head. Draw her mouth in the middle.

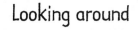

Hungry dinosaurs

Use a pencil.

The paint will run a little.

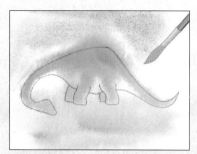

1. Draw a dinosaur's head on a piece of white paper. Add a long neck, a rounded body and a tail. Then, draw a tummy and four short legs.

2. Dip a paintbrush into clean water, then brush it all over the paper. Mix some watery green paint. Then, blob it all over the dinosaur, like this.

3. Dip the brush back into the paint and blob it all over the ground beneath the dinosaur. Mix some watery blue paint, then blob it on for the sky.

Use ideas from this picture to draw your own dinosaur scene.

You could draw a baby dinosaur on its mother's back.

10

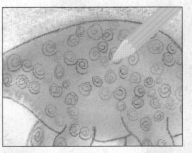

4. When the paint is dry, draw around the dinosaur with a green pencil. Add a black dot for an eye. Then, add a green mouth, nostrils and toenails.

5. For patterns on the neck, legs, body and tail, draw lots of little spirals with pencils. Use different shades of green and blue, if you have them.

6. Use a green pencil to draw some leaves in the dinosaur's mouth. Then, draw lines for the stems of ferns and add lots of loops for leaves.

For a prehistoric tree, paint a brown line for the trunk and a blob for leaves on the wet paper.

For a Christmassy scene, you could add Santa and his reindeer in the sky.

Draw different shapes of buildings.

A snowy hill

1. Draw a curve for a hill on a piece of dark blue paper. Fill it in with thick white paint. Then, draw stars in the sky with a white pencil or chalk.

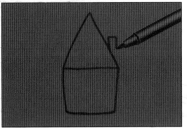

2. Using a dark pink felt-tip pen, draw a square for a house on a piece of pink or purple paper. Add a pointed roof and a chimney.

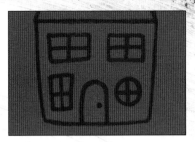

3. Draw a door, then add a dot for a handle. Then, draw several different shapes for windows. Add crossed lines inside each one.

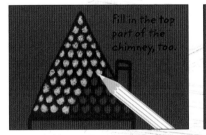

Fill in the top part of the chimney, too.

4. Draw rows of 'U' shapes on the roof for tiles. Then, fill in the tiles with a white pencil. Make sure that you don't go over any of the pen lines.

5. Fill in the wall of the house with a lilac pencil. Make the windows orange and blue, and the door red. Then, fill in the chimney with lilac.

6. Draw a large triangle for a tree with a dark pink felt-tip pen. Add a little rectangle at the bottom of the tree for the trunk, like this.

7. For branches, draw three zigzag lines across the tree. Then, draw a star at the top of the tree. Fill it in with an orange pencil.

Use darker shades for the lower branches.

8. Fill in the top part of the tree with a white pencil. Then, use different shades of blue and green pencils to fill in the rest of the branches.

9. Draw several more houses and trees in the same way. Cut them out and arrange them on the snowy hill. Then, glue them on.

Pretty princesses

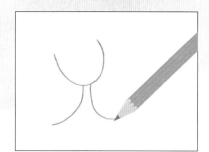

1. Using a pencil, draw a 'U' shape for a princess's face, near to the top of a piece of white paper. Then, add two long curves for her neck.

2. Draw two curves at the top of the face for a parting in the hair. Add the rest of the hair. Draw a curved neckline, then add a 'V' shape for a bodice.

You could draw a princess carrying a bag, a fan or even a little dog.

Start to draw the skirt here.

3. Starting about halfway up the bodice, draw two curves for a skirt. Add a curve for the bottom edge. Then, draw two curved lines on the skirt.

4. For the sleeves, draw two ovals next to the neckline. Add two shapes below them, with frilly bottom edges. Draw little shapes for hands, too.

Draw thin lines on the skirt, too.

5. Draw over all the lines with felt-tip pens. Draw thick bands around the princess's neckline, sleeves, waist and skirt. Then, fill in her hair.

The dress above had pink and orange pencil lines added to the yellow part of the skirt.

Don't brush over the thick bands.

6. Dip a paintbrush into clean water. Carefully brush over the pen lines so that the ink runs. Brush the watery ink around so that it fills each shape.

You could add ribbons in her hair.

7. When the ink is dry, draw eyes with a black felt-tip pen. Use pencils to draw a nose, lips and cheeks. Then, add a crown with a gold pen.

8. Use pencils to draw over all the lines again. Then, decorate the princess's dress with bows and frilly lace. Add spots and patterns with a gold pen, too.

Simple dinosaurs

Use this shape for long-necked dinosaurs such as diplodocus and plateosaurus.

These dinosaurs were drawn using the triceratops shapes in the panel on the opposite page.

1. For a dinosaur with a long neck, draw a large oval in the middle of some white paper. Add two smaller ovals for the tops of the legs, like this.

2. Draw a small oval for the head, above and to the right of the body. Draw a long neck curving up to the head. Then, add a long tail.

Make these legs a little shorter.

3. Draw two legs coming down from the small ovals you drew in step 1. Then, add the other two legs, to the right of the ones you have just drawn.

Draw an upright shape like this for a tyrannosaurus rex.

Follow the shapes shown above to draw a dinosaur standing on its back legs. Give it very short arms.

For a triceratops, draw an oval for its head at the same height as the oval for its back leg.

Draw two ovals for the head and body of a flying dinosaur. Then, add wings and a beak.

This green dinosaur is a stegosaur.

Add spikes on the tail, too.

4. Draw over the outline and around the legs with a green pencil. Add an eye and a mouth. Then, erase all of the lead pencil lines.

5. Fill in the dinosaur with watery green paint. While the paint is still wet, add darker blobs on the back, neck and tail. Leave the paint to dry.

Follow these shapes to draw a stegosaur. Draw diamond shapes along its back.

You could draw a line of ovals for footprints in the snow.

Snowy skaters

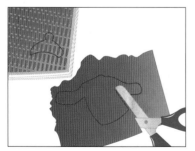

1. Rip pictures of different clothes from old magazines. Using a pencil, draw a hat and a sweater on the pictures. Then, cut out the shapes.

Draw the ear halfway down the head.

2. Glue the sweater onto a large piece of white paper. Draw an oval head above it with a blue felt-tip pen. Then, add two eyes and an ear.

3. Draw a mouth and a shape for hair, then fill them in. Use a paler pen to draw mittens at the end of the sleeves. Then, draw a skirt and fill it in, too.

Add birds and animals with a pale blue felt-tip pen.

This dog's scarf was cut from paper and its body was drawn with a pen.

4. Draw two curved legs, then add feet. Fill in the legs and feet. Then, draw two short lines and a curved blade for each ice skate.

5. Glue the hat onto the top of the skater's head. Then, draw several more skaters in the same way, using ideas from the big picture above.

6. Draw a little fence around the skaters for the edge of the pond. Draw curved lines for tracks on the ice. Then, add trees behind the pond.

Rainy day fairies

Leave space on your paper to draw more fairies.

Draw a star at the end of the wand.

The wax crayon is shown here in yellow so that you can see it.

1. Using a pencil, draw a circle for a fairy's head on white paper. Draw a dress with a wavy bottom edge. Then, add arms, legs and wings, like this.

2. Draw the fairy's hair, eyes and eyelashes. Draw a nose and a big smile, then add little heart-shaped lips on the smile. Add a wand in her hand, too.

3. Draw more fairies in the same way. Add some leaves and toadstools for umbrellas. Then, use a white wax crayon to draw lines for raindrops.

You could add flowers, stars and some little creatures around your fairies.

The raindrops show through the paint.

4. Brush water all over the paper. Then, dab watery pink paint on top so that it spreads out in the water. Dab on some yellow paint, too.

5. Leave the paint to dry. Then, draw over all the pencil lines with different felt-tip pens. Add patterns on the fairies' dresses, too.

6. Dip a thin paintbrush into clean water. Then, brush over the pen lines so that the ink runs. Rinse your brush after you do each part of a fairy.

Draw a heart instead of a star at the end of a wand.

One of the fairies could be wearing glasses.

Meerkats

1. Draw a bean shape for a meerkat's head on white paper. Add a shape for its nose. Then, draw curving lines for the body and legs.

Add little claws on all the paws.

2. Draw the back legs and the tail. Then, add the front legs curving in to the middle of the body. Draw a mound and grass behind the meerkat.

3. Erase the pencil lines inside the head. Draw ovals for the eyes and add dots inside for pupils. Then, add the nose, mouth and ear.

Paint the nose, too.

4. Brush watery pale orange paint along the top of the head, the sides of the body and the tail. Paint the mound and grass with yellow paint.

5. Mix some watery brown paint. Brush it down the front of the body and on the front paws. Paint the ear and add patches around the eyes, too.

This baby meerkat was drawn using the same shapes as an adult meerkat.

If you want to draw a scene, draw the meerkats, mounds and grass, first. Then, fill everything in with watery paints.

Draw a big black
mouth for a
roaring lion.

Fierce lions

1. Mix orange paint by adding
a little red to some yellow
paint. Paint a circle for a
lion's head. Add a neck, then
paint an oval for the body.

2. Paint four thick lines for legs
and add four paws. Then, add
a blob for the end of the tail,
a little way from the body.
Leave the paint to dry.

3. Draw a line for the tail with
an orange pencil. Scribble a
mane around the lion's head.
Scribble over the mane again
with a darker orange pencil.

4. Using a thin black pen,
draw eyes and a long nose.
Then, add a mouth, ears and
whiskers. Draw lines on the
paws and tail, like this.

Draw a lioness
without a mane.

Busy trucks

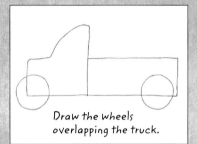

Draw the wheels overlapping the truck.

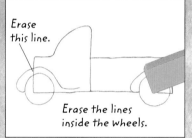

Erase this line.

Erase the lines inside the wheels.

Add lines on the wheels and circles on the hubcaps.

1. Pressing lightly with a pencil, draw a shape for a truck's cab. Draw a rectangle next to it for the back of the truck, then add two wheels.

2. Add curved lines over the wheels for mudguards. Then, erase the lines where the wheels and mudguards overlap the truck.

3. Draw a window, a door and a headlight on the cab. Add a bumper at the back of the truck. Then, draw a round hubcap on each wheel.

Look at this picture for more ideas of things to draw.

For a truck filled with bananas, paint a big yellow shape, then draw bananas on top with an orange pencil.

Draw some slices of melon, too.

4. Draw a driver in the truck's window and add a steering wheel. Then, draw lots of circles for watermelons in the back of the truck.

5. Fill in the truck with bright runny paints. Paint the wheels with watery black paint. Then, fill in the driver and the watermelons.

6. When the paint is dry, draw over all the lines with bright pencils. Add lines on the watermelons and on the back of the truck, too.

You could draw animals or plants in the back of a truck.

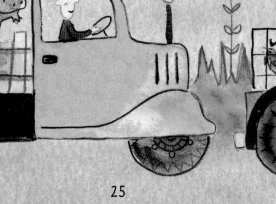

Leaping ballerinas

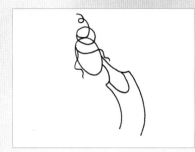

Draw a spiral for hair on top of the head.

1. Use a thin black felt-tip pen to draw an oval for a ballerina's head. Draw it about a third of the way down a piece of paper. Then, add some curling hair.

You could draw your ballerina on white, pale pink or lilac paper.

Use the ideas shown here to draw other leaping ballerinas.

2. Draw two curved lines for the neck. Join the lines with a 'U' shape for the neckline of a tutu. Then, draw two more curved lines for the body.

3. Using a pink felt-tip pen, draw a circle for each sleeve. Add a spiral inside each one. Then, draw looping lines below the body for the skirt.

4. Dip a paintbrush into clean water. Gently brush over all the pink pen lines so that the ink runs. Then, leave your picture to dry completely.

Start here.

5. Starting at the right-hand edge of the tutu, draw a bent leg with a pointed foot. Then, add the other leg at the same angle. Draw ballet shoes, too.

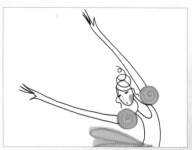

6. Draw two long arms with stretched-out fingers. Add two black curves for eyes. Then, draw a nose, a mouth and cheeks with a pink pencil.

Add a pink
band on each
sleeve.

7. Fill in the bodice of the tutu
with a pink pencil. Fill in the
ballet shoes and the hair, too.
Then, add ribbons around the
legs with the black pen.

*You could draw lots
of little hearts around
your ballerina.*

Big bear and baby bear

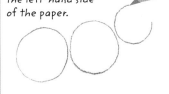
Start drawing near the left-hand side of the paper.

1. For a baby polar bear, draw a circle on white paper. Add a second circle next to it. Then, draw a slightly smaller circle to one side, for the head.

2. Join the two larger circles together with curved lines. Add two shorter lines for the neck. Then, draw shapes for the bear's ear and snout.

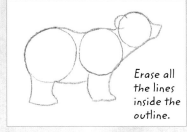
Erase all the lines inside the outline.

3. Draw a leg coming down from each of the larger circles. Then, draw around the outline of the bear with a blue pencil. Erase the lead pencil lines.

Draw the mother bear's head near the baby bear.

4. Draw a circle for a mother bear's head. Add a bigger slanted oval for the shoulder. Then, draw a big circle for the back of the body.

Draw a line for the ground, too.

5. Draw curves for the neck and body, then add a snout and an ear. Draw over the shapes with a blue pencil and erase the lead pencil lines.

To make the mother bear look really furry, draw long wavy yellow lines on her body.

6. Using a clean paintbrush, brush water around the bears. While the paper is wet, blob watery pale blue paint onto the background, for the sky.

7. Rinse your paintbrush. Then, brush very pale yellow paint just inside the outline of each polar bear. Leave the paint to dry completely.

8. Use a blue pencil to draw the bears' faces. Draw short lines along the outlines for fur. Then, add more fur on the bodies with a yellow pencil.

Diving dinosaurs

Try drawing
different sizes
of dinosaurs
diving together.

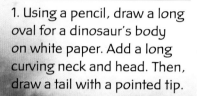

Use a dark blue
felt-tip pen.

1. Using a pencil, draw a long oval for a dinosaur's body on white paper. Add a long curving neck and head. Then, draw a tail with a pointed tip.

2. Add two flippers at each end of the body. Then draw over the outline with a felt-tip pen. Erase the pencil lines, then draw more dinosaurs.

Draw each
dinosaur with
its flippers at a
different angle.

The ink will run.

3. Dip a large paintbrush into clean water. Brush it all over your paper to make a watery background. Then, leave the paper to dry a little.

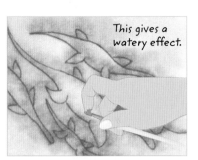

This gives a watery effect.

4. While the paper is still damp, dip a thin paintbrush into the water. Pull a finger back over the bristles to spray water all over your picture.

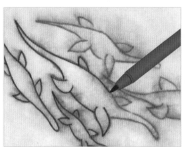

5. Leave your picture to dry completely. Then, draw over the outline of each dinosaur again with the dark blue felt-tip pen.

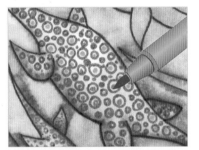

6. Use bright purple, blue and pink felt-tip pens to draw circles all over the dinosaurs' bodies. Then, add bright spots inside the circles.

7. Dip the thin paintbrush into some clean water. Brush it over the circles and spots so that the ink runs. Try not to brush over the outlines.

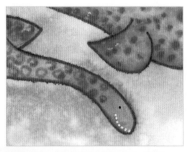

8. Leave the ink to dry. Then, add a row of little teeth on each dinosaur with thick white paint or correcting fluid. Draw a black dot for an eye.

Draw two eyes for a dinosaur turning its head to the side.

Mermaids on rocks

Add lines on the rock for cracks.

1. For the sea, brush watery blue paint across the bottom of a piece of white paper. Add two shapes for rocks above it. Then, leave the paint to dry.

2. Paint a tail, overlapping one of the rocks. Paint a shape for a bikini top. Then, add a round face, a tummy and some hair. Let the paint dry.

3. Draw around the bikini top and the tail with a blue pen, but don't follow the edges exactly. Use a black pen to draw a face. Then, draw around the rock.

You could use the ideas shown here to draw mermaids doing different things.

4. Draw one arm with the hand leaning on the rock. Draw the other arm waving. Add lots of little scales on the tail. Then, draw curly lines on the hair.

5. For a diving mermaid, paint the shapes as you did in step 2, but arrange them like this. Draw the arms stretching out in front. Then, add outlines with pens.

6. Paint simple shapes for the body and tail of a fish. Draw the outline, then add an eye, a mouth and fins. Draw lots of curly waves with a blue pen.

Draw curves like these, for seagulls in the sky.

Try drawing mermaids with different hairstyles.

Mischievous monkeys

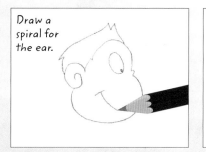

Draw a spiral for the ear.

1. Draw a curve for a monkey's forehead on white paper. Add a nose and an ear, then draw a chin. Draw fur on the head, then add an eye and a mouth.

Add little peaks along the outline of the arms for fur.

2. Draw two curving lines for an arm, then add a little hand. Draw the other arm with thin oval fingers. Add a vine for the monkey to hang from.

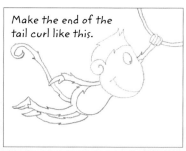

Make the end of the tail curl like this.

3. Draw a rounded shape for a tummy. Add the rest of the body around it. Then, draw curved legs and add the feet. Draw a long curling tail, too.

Fill in the vine, too.

4. Fill in the monkey using different shades of watery brown paint. When the paint is dry, draw over the pencil lines with a brown felt-tip pen.

For a surprised monkey, draw an oval mouth.

For a scene like this, draw everything first, then fill in the picture with paints. Add outlines when the paint is dry.

You could add 'whoosh' lines to show that a monkey is swinging through the air.

Sitting monkey

1. Draw two arches for the forehead, then add spirals for ears. Draw a big chin and fur on the head. Then, draw the eyes, nose and mouth.

2. Draw a tummy and add the rest of the body around it. Draw two arms, with ovals for fingers. Add the legs and tail, then draw a vine, like this.

3. Use watery paints to fill in the monkey and the vine. Leave all the paint to dry, then use felt-tip pens to draw over the pencil lines.

Big yellow truck

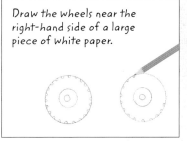

Draw the wheels near the right-hand side of a large piece of white paper.

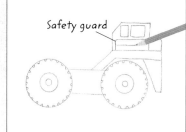

Safety guard

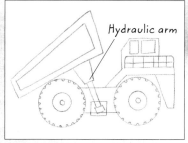

Hydraulic arm

1. Using a pencil, draw two big circles for wheels. Add a hubcap on each wheel. Draw lots of tiny half circles around the wheels, for the tread.

You could draw diggers and trucks in the background, too.

2. Draw two lines between the wheels. Then, draw a big mudguard over the front wheel. Draw a cab, then add windows and a safety guard.

3. For a container, draw a diagonal line above the back wheel. Draw the rest of the container above the line, then add a hydraulic arm below it.

When you've drawn over the pencil lines, add a driver in the cab.

Draw lots of bolts and rivets on your truck and its hubcaps.

The paint will run a little.

Pull your finger back over the bristles.

4. Using a clean paintbrush, brush water over the paper. Then, dip the brush into watery yellow paint and blob it onto the truck and hubcaps.

5. Blob watery black paint onto the truck's wheels. Then, brush dust clouds and swirls at the back of the truck, like this. Leave the paint to dry.

6. Dip a paintbrush into black paint and splatter it over the dust clouds, like this. Then, roughly draw over the pencil lines with a thin black pen.

Fingerprinted dinosaurs

Smear your finger on the paper to make the shapes.

1. Spread green paint on an old plate, then dip a finger into it. Go around and around on a piece of paper to paint a dinosaur's head and body.

2. Dip your finger back into the paint. Fingerprint two legs at the bottom of the body. Use a paintbrush to paint a long neck and a pointed tail.

3. Leave the paint to dry. Then, fingerprint dark green spines along the dinosaur's back. Fingerprint blue spots on the body, too.

Don't draw around the spines.

4. Paint white ovals for eyes and let them dry. Then, draw around the eyes with a felt-tip pen. Add pupils and nostrils, then draw around the head.

5. Draw around the neck, legs, tummy and tail. Then, draw along the back, straight through the spines. Add little toenails on the feet, too.

Add spots or stripes with a chalk pastel.

Try printing dinosaurs in different positions.

Cartoon dinosaurs

Draw dots in ovals for worried eyes.

Draw the dot at the top of the eye for a scared expression.

The lines across this dinosaur's neck show that it is turning its head quickly.

1. Draw an oval on white paper for a dinosaur's head. Add a mouth and an eye with a dot in it. Draw two curved lines that join up at the tail.

Draw lines to help it look as if the leaves are falling.

Draw eyes close together and add pointed teeth for a fierce look.

2. Draw two curved lines for a leg, then add two shorter curves for a foot. Draw the other leg, then add claws. Draw spikes along the back.

Fill in the dinosaur with felt-tip pens.

3. Draw two bent arms on the body, then add fingers. Draw over the outlines with a thick black felt-tip pen. Then, erase any remaining pencil lines.

Exaggerate the length of the dinosaur's neck.

You could add circles for scales on a dinosaur's back.

Draw lines behind a dinosaur to make it look as if it's running.

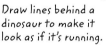

Draw a shadow under a dinosaur to show that it is leaping off the ground.

Fairy flower garden

1. For a fairy garden, cut pages from old magazines that have pictures of flowers on them. Then, cut around some individual flowers and leaves.

2. Glue the flowers and leaves onto a large piece of paper. Make some of them overlap, but leave spaces for drawing fairies, too.

Draw a fairy flying between two flowers.

If you draw a fairy with her arms in the air, she looks as if she is waving or jumping up.

40

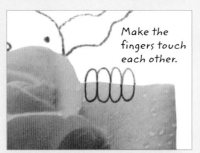

3. Draw a half circle for the top of a fairy's face peeking out from behind a flower. Add two eyes and a little nose. Then, draw the fairy's hair.

4. For fingers, draw four long ovals in a row, like this. Make them overlap the edge of the flower, to look as if they are curling over the petal.

Make the fingers touch each other.

5. You could also draw a fairy looking around the side of a flower. Just draw part of her body – the rest of it is hidden behind the flower.

Try drawing different expressions, such as an oval mouth for a surprised fairy.

Use a blue felt-tip pen to draw around the wings.

6. Draw more fairies between the flowers. Then, carefully fill them in with felt-tip pens or paints. Draw around them with a black felt-tip pen.

Countryside painting

Draw the tractor near the bottom of the paper.

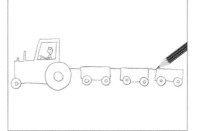

Draw the tree a little way from the tractor.

1. Using a pencil, draw the cab and engine of a tractor on white paper. Add wheels, a window, and exhaust pipes. Then, draw a driver.

2. Draw a little trailer behind the tractor and add wheels. Draw two more trailers next to it. Then, join the trailers and the tractor with lines.

3. Draw a circle for a tree. Add a trunk and branches below it. Draw a tall ladder next to the tree. Then, draw a man with a basket on his back.

Use the ideas in this picture to paint a large scene.

You could paint a house and hills in the background.

Don't worry if the field overlaps the tractor.

Use the tip of a thin paintbrush.

4. Mix brown paint with some water on an old plate. Paint a shape for a field. Then, fill in the tree with watery green paint. Leave the paint to dry.

5. Paint the tractor, trailers, tree trunk and ladder with thicker paint. Paint the driver and the man on the ladder. Then, leave the paint to dry.

6. Draw faces with a thin black pen. Add lines on the tractor with a white pencil. Draw lines on the field, and fruit and leaves on the tree.

Draw lots of apple trees for an orchard.

Crocodile swamp

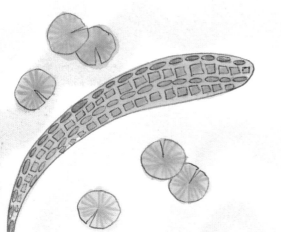

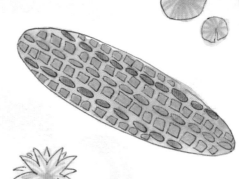

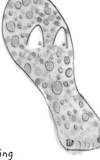

Join the lines at the top.

1. Using a pencil, draw a long curving line on white paper for one side of a crocodile's body. Then, draw another line next to it, like this.

2. Draw two small arches for the eyes. Add a long nose, then draw a wavy line for the mouth. Draw the crocodile's bottom jaw below the mouth.

For a swimming crocodile, draw shapes for the head, body and tail. The rest of the crocodile is hidden under the water.

The fourth leg is hidden behind the body.

Try not to smudge the pen lines.

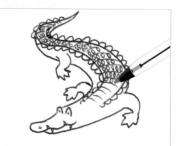

3. Draw two legs near the head, one on each side of the body. Make them thick and chunky, with pointed claws. Draw a leg near the tail, too.

4. Draw around the legs with a ballpoint pen. Then, draw around the rest of the crocodile. Carefully erase the pencil lines inside the legs.

5. Draw some teeth, a nostril and dots in the eyes. Add two lines curving along the crocodile's back. Then, draw lots of scales on the body.

Use the ideas on these pages for different patterns of scales to draw on a crocodile.

This background was drawn with a ballpoint pen, then filled in with watery paints.

Only brush inside the crocodile's outline.

6. Use different shades of green felt-tip pens to fill in the scales. Add lots of spots and lines on the rest of the crocodile, too.

7. Dip a paintbrush into clean water. Then, carefully brush it all over the crocodile's body, so that the inks from the lines and spots bleed together.

A ballet class

Use watery paint to paint reflections on the mirror.

Dancers in a ballet class hold onto a barre to help them balance.

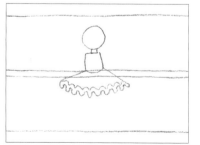

1. Draw a long rectangle for a mirror. Add two lines across the middle for a rail, called a barre. Then, draw a ballerina's head, neck and tutu, like this.

Erase the barre where the ballerina overlaps it.

2. Draw one arm holding onto the barre and the other one curving above the head. Draw one straight leg and the other one bent at the knee.

3. Draw hair on the ballerina's head. Add loops for a tiara on top of her head, then add a bun above the tiara. Draw her face and ringlets, too.

Draw little curved lines to show that a ballerina's arms are moving.

Fill in between the wavy lines of the tutus with a darker shade of paint.

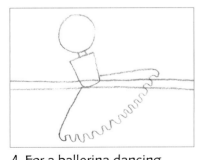

4. For a ballerina dancing sideways, draw the bodice of her tutu leaning to one side. Add the skirt below it, then draw her head and neck.

Erase these lines.

5. Draw one arm along the top of the barre and the other one curving up. Add some hair on the head, too. Erase the barre where the ballerina overlaps it.

6. Draw legs, ballet shoes and a sash. Paint the ballerinas with watery paints and let the paint dry. Then, draw over all the lines with felt-tip pens.

Patterned dinosaurs

For a scene like this, paint a large hill and some sky. Then, cut out dinosaurs and glue them on top.

1. Use a pencil to draw the outline of a dinosaur on a piece of green paper. Add eyes, a mouth, spikes on the tail, then toenails on the feet.

Use felt-tip pens to draw ferns and dragonflies.

2. Draw a diamond shape on the middle of the back, for a bony plate. Then, draw smaller plates on both sides of the middle one, like this.

3. Draw over the pencil lines with a felt-tip pen. Add rows of 'U' shapes on the body for scales. Then, add teeth with correcting fluid or white paint.

4. Draw long lines on the bony plates with green pens. Add short lines on the plates, spikes and toenails. Fill in some of the scales, too.

5. For a dinosaur with a frill, draw several curved lines along its back. Then, join the ends of the lines with shorter curved lines, like this.

Add dots on the spines and toenails.

6. You could also draw spines along a dinosaur's back. Fill in the spines and toenails. Then, draw lots of spirals on the dinosaur's body.

Moonlit fairies

Paint lots of
little dots for
stars around
the fairies.

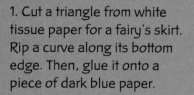

1. Cut a triangle from white tissue paper for a fairy's skirt. Rip a curve along its bottom edge. Then, glue it onto a piece of dark blue paper.

2. Use a white chalk or chalk pastel to draw the top layer of the skirt, overlapping the tissue paper. Add some lines for pleats in the skirt.

3. Cut another piece of tissue paper for the body and glue it on. Then, use the white chalk to draw the fairy's wings on either side of the body.

4. To make the wings and skirt look transparent, rub the chalk lines to smudge them. Draw over the outlines again, and add more lines inside the shapes.

5. Using a thin paintbrush, paint the fairy's head and neck. Paint two straight lines for arms. Then, paint several wavy lines for hair.

For a glowing moon, draw a circle with a chalk and smudge it with your finger. Then, paint the middle with yellow paint.

6. Draw a line with the white chalk for the fairy's wand. Then, paint several little yellow lines coming out from the end of it, for a star.

7. Leave the paint to dry completely. Then, draw the fairy's eyes, nose and lips with felt-tip pens. Add little pink ovals on her cheeks, too.

If you draw fairies at different angles, it makes them look as if they are flying.

Tobogganing

Erase the lines where the trees overlap the wavy line.

1. Using a pencil, draw a long wavy line across a piece of white paper, for hills. Then, draw some triangular-shaped trees along the line.

2. For a girl pulling a toboggan, draw a circle for a head. Add the body, arms and hands. Then, draw the legs and feet, like this.

3. Draw a hat on the girl's head, then add some hair. Draw her eyes, nose and mouth, too. Then, add a line around her neck for a scarf.

4. Draw a shape next to the girl's foot for a toboggan. Add a curve along its front edge. Then, draw lines joining the toboggan to her hand.

5. Draw a seat and footrests on the toboggan. Then, draw some stripes on the girl's clothes. Add pockets and buttons on her coat, too.

Use ideas from this picture to draw your own snowy scene.

You could draw a boy making a snowman.

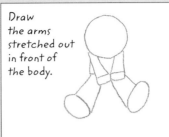

Draw the arms stretched out in front of the body.

6. Fill in the girl and the toboggan with lots of different felt-tip pens. Then, draw over all the outlines with a thin black pen.

7. For someone sitting on a toboggan, draw a round head. Add the body, arms and legs. Then, draw two ovals for feet facing up, like this.

8. Draw a shape around the body for a toboggan. Draw a line for the front edge, then add more lines across it. Add curved runners at the front.

9. Draw a hat and some ears. Draw hair flowing out on each side of the head. Add eyes, a nose and a mouth. Then, fill in the drawing.

Leave parts of the trees white, for snow.

Draw footprints and tracks in the snow with a light blue felt-tip pen.

53

Red tractor

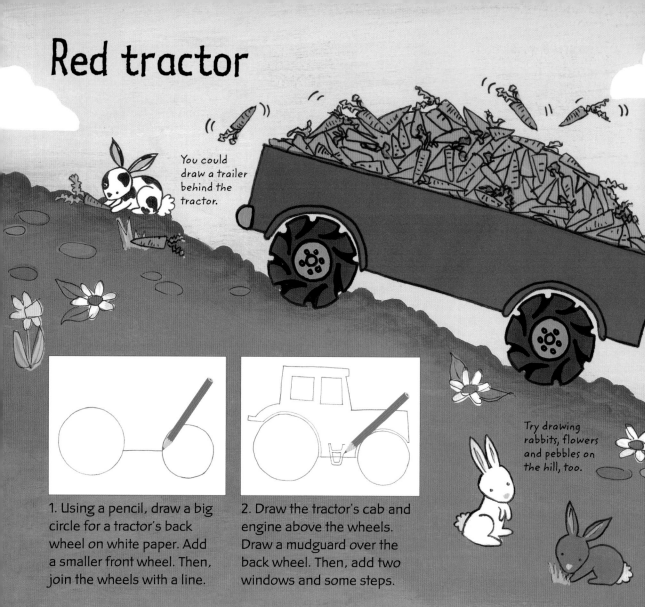

You could draw a trailer behind the tractor.

Try drawing rabbits, flowers and pebbles on the hill, too.

1. Using a pencil, draw a big circle for a tractor's back wheel on white paper. Add a smaller front wheel. Then, join the wheels with a line.

2. Draw the tractor's cab and engine above the wheels. Draw a mudguard over the back wheel. Then, add two windows and some steps.

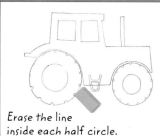

Erase the line inside each half circle.

3. Draw a round hubcap on each wheel. Then, draw lots of tiny half circles around the wheels, for the tread. Add an exhaust pipe on the engine.

4. Fill in the main part of the tractor with thick red paint. Paint the wheels and exhaust pipe. Then, fill in the steps and hubcaps, too.

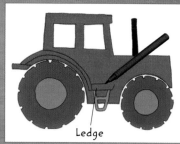

Ledge

5. Leave the paint to dry. Then, draw over the outlines with a black pen. Draw curved lines for the mudguard, and add a ledge above the steps.

For a scene like this, draw a tractor, then add a line for a hill. Then, fill everything in with paints.

6. Draw a door around the front window. Add frames around both windows. Then, draw a trim, a radiator grill and a vent on the engine.

7. For the tread on the wheels, draw a black shape curving in from each tiny half circle. Then, add circles and bolts on the hubcaps.

8. Using a pencil, draw a driver in the front window. Draw over all the lines with a thin black pen. Then, fill in the driver with felt-tip pens.

Little princesses

1. Using a pencil, draw a circle for a princess's head. Add her face and ears. Then, draw the bodice and skirt of her dress. Add little shapes for shoes.

Draw a spiral inside each circle.

2. For the princess's hair, draw lines on her head. Add a circle above each ear. Then, draw puffed sleeves on the dress. Add her arms and hands, too.

Let the paint dry before you draw over the lines.

3. Draw a crown, then add patterns and lace on the dress. Fill in the princess with watery paints. Then, draw over the lines with a black felt-tip pen.

Use the ideas shown in this picture to draw princesses doing different things.

You could draw three princesses holding hands.

4. For a princess peeking out from behind a rose bush, draw the head and dress leaning over a little. Draw her arms at an angle, too.

5. Draw a shape for a bush overlapping the princess's skirt and arm. Then, erase the parts of the skirt and arm that are inside the bush.

6. Draw circles on the bush for roses. Add a spiral in each one. Fill in your drawing with paints. When it's dry, draw over the outlines with a pen.

For a pond like this, draw the outline first, then add the grass, lily pads, fish and boat before you fill it in.

Draw a princess picking flowers.

Try drawing lots of different styles of crowns and tiaras.

57

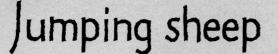

Jumping sheep

Press harder when you draw the head, ears and legs.

1. Pressing lightly with a purple pencil, draw a circle for a sheep's body on pink paper. Draw the head, then add the ears and legs.

2. Draw lots of big spirals all over the sheep's body to look like curling wool. Then, draw a spiral above the back legs for the tail.

3. Use a darker pencil to draw a small 'V' for the nose. Add a curling mouth below it. Draw ovals for the eyes, then add dots inside them for pupils.

4. Use a white chalk or chalk pastel to fill in the body and the tail. Then, rub the chalk a little, to smudge it and make the edges blurred.

5. Fill in the head, ears and legs with a purple chalk, then smudge them a little. Add white inside the eyes and pink spots on the cheeks.

6. Use a yellow chalk to draw a line along the tummy and a little line under the tail. Then, smudge the yellow lines into the white chalk a little.

You could draw a
sheep counting the
jumping sheep.

The hill, moon and stars
in this picture were
drawn after the sheep,
then filled in with chalks.

Tractor in the snow

For a snowy landscape, draw hills with trees on them.

Draw rabbits in the snow and birds in the trees.

Press lightly with a pencil.

Shake off any extra glitter mixture.

1. Draw the cab and engine of a tractor. Then, draw wheels, a mudguard, a window and exhaust pipes. Add wavy lines for tracks behind the tractor.

2. Brush water on the tractor, but not on the window. Blob watery paint onto the tractor. Let it dry. Draw over the lines with a thin pen and add a driver.

3. For glittery tracks, mix some sugar with a little glitter. Brush white glue over the tracks, then sprinkle the glitter mixture over the glue.

You could add a dog in the back of the tractor.

Monster trucks

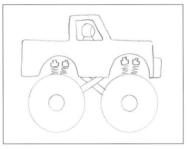

1. Draw a truck with a cab at the top and wheel arches at the bottom. Add a bumper, then draw two giant wheels, with hubcaps in the middle.

2. Draw a window with a driver inside. Then, draw two shock absorbers above each wheel. Add lines for a crossbar below the truck.

3. Add headlights and a flag. Then, draw patterns on the truck and fill it in with felt-tip pens. Draw over the outlines with a black felt-tip pen.

Draw different shapes for trucks, then add some of the patterns shown here.

Add dust clouds with a black felt-tip pen.

For an angry-looking dinosaur like the one above, draw slanted eyebrows above the eyes.

Potato-printed dinosaurs

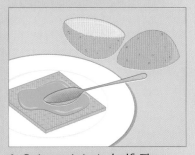

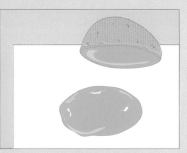

Add a mouth, nostrils and a pupil in the eye, too.

1. Cut a potato in half. Then, lay a piece of kitchen sponge cloth on an old plate. Using an old spoon, spread thick paint on the sponge.

2. Press the flat side of one of the pieces of potato into the paint. Press it firmly onto a piece of paper, then lift it off. Leave the paint to dry.

3. Use a green pencil or wax crayon to draw a neck. Then, paint a white eye. When it is dry, draw around everything with a black wax crayon.

For a dinosaur like the one below, paint a pointed nose and draw a frill.

The pink cheeks on these dinosaurs were drawn with a pink chalk pastel.

Draw spirals in
the eyes of a
dizzy dinosaur.

You could add spots or
stripes on your dinosaur
with pencils or crayons.

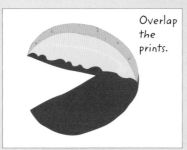

Overlap
the
prints.

4. For a dinosaur with a wide mouth, make one print. Turn the potato, then print it again, across the first print. Paint the mouth, then draw the teeth.

5. For a dinosaur with an open mouth, cut a piece of potato in half again. Use one of the pieces to print a bottom jaw. Then, print the top jaw, too.

6. You could also use one of the smaller pieces of potato to print a head like this. Draw a mouth a little way above the straight edge.

For a picture with lots
of dinosaurs, do all
the potato prints first.
Draw their necks and
outline them when the
paint is dry.

Fairytale princess

You could draw some butterflies and dragonflies around the princess.

These clouds were drawn with a white wax crayon, then the sky was painted over them.

Draw some grasses and reeds around the pond.

To do a big scene like this, draw the princess and the frog, then add the pond.

1. Use a green pencil to draw two ovals for a princess's skirt. Add a purple curve between them. Then, draw a bodice, sleeves and shoes.

2. Draw the princess's neck, face and hair with an ordinary lead pencil. Use bright pencils to draw her crown, arms, and a flower in her hands.

3. Use green, orange and pink wax crayons to draw patterns on the princess's skirt. Then, draw pink lines on her hair. Add circles on her cheeks, too.

Paint inside the crayon lines.

4. Mix some watery purple paint. Then, fill in the bodice, sleeves, and parts of the skirt. Fill in the rest of the skirt with other shades of watery paint.

5. Paint the face, arms, shoes and crown. Then, paint the hair. When all the paint is dry, draw over the eyes, nose, mouth and skirt again.

Use different shades of green crayons.

6. For a frog prince, draw the outline of a frog. Draw a face and a crown. Add green spots and pink cheeks with wax crayons. Then, add a lily pad.

The wax crayon will resist the paint.

7. Paint the frog and the lily pad using different shades of watery paint. When the paint is dry, draw over the pencil and crayon lines again.

Fairy paperchain

To make a long line
of fairies, tape two
paperchains together.

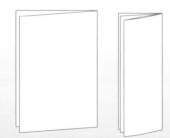

1. Cut a long rectangle of thin paper. Fold it in half, so that the shorter edges meet. Then, fold the paper in half again. Crease the folds really well.

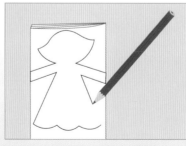

2. Draw a shape for a fairy's hair on the folded paper. Then, draw her arms, making them touch each side of the paper. Draw her dress, too.

3. Cut around your drawing, but don't cut along the folds at the ends of the arms. Then, carefully unfold the paper to make a chain of four fairies.

Try adding patterns using paper shapes and a gold pen.

You could cut a star from foil instead of a crown.

Cut out and glue on foil crowns, too.

4. Fill in the fairies' hair and hands with felt-tip pens. Then, draw four faces on a separate piece of paper. Cut them out and glue them onto the fairies.

5. Cut some strips of patterned paper from old magazines and glue them onto the dresses. Then, draw patterns on the dresses with felt-tip pens.

6. Fold a piece of kitchen foil as you did in step 1. Draw a set of wings against the fold. Cut them out, then glue them onto the backs of the fairies.

Printed reindeer

1. Glue a piece of a kitchen sponge onto a piece of thin cardboard. Draw shapes for a reindeer's body and head on the cardboard.

2. Using scissors, carefully cut out both shapes. Then, spread some thick red paint on an old plate. Dip the body shape into the paint.

3. To print the body, press the sponge onto a piece of paper. Then, dip the head shape into the paint. Print it next to the body, like this.

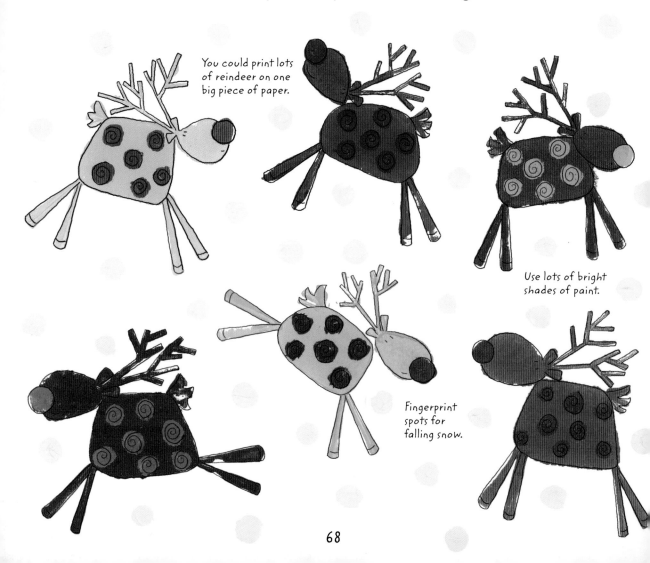

You could print lots of reindeer on one big piece of paper.

Use lots of bright shades of paint.

Fingerprint spots for falling snow.

Try printing the shapes at different angles for running and jumping reindeer.

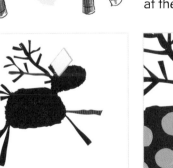

Twist the cardboard at one end as you print.

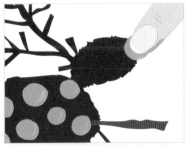

4. To print the reindeer's legs, cut a rectangle from thick cardboard. Dip one edge into the paint, then print four legs at the bottom of the body.

5. Dip the cardboard into the paint again. Print two lines on the head for the antlers. Then, print two shorter lines with a smaller piece of cardboard.

6. Print lots more short lines on the antlers. Add three lines for the tail, too. Then, print the ears, twisting the cardboard a little as you print.

7. Spread some light blue paint on the plate. Then, dip a finger into the paint. Print several spots on the body, and one on the nose.

You could draw little spirals on the spots.

8. When the paint is dry, draw around the reindeer with a thin black felt-tip pen. Then, add a mouth, lines for hooves and dots for eyes.

Dinosaur party

Make the nose look like a beak.

1. Using a pencil, draw a nose and mouth, then add a bottom jaw. Draw a wavy frill at the back of the head. Then, add eyes and eyebrows.

The fourth leg is hidden behind the body.

2. Starting at the head, draw a fat body shape with a pointed tail. Then, draw two legs at the front of the body, and one near the tail.

Add presents and balloons to make your picture look like a party.

Look at this picture for ideas of other dinosaurs you could draw.

3. Brush clean water over the dinosaur. Blob watery paint onto the water so that it runs. Then, blob more paint along the tummy and the tail.

Draw spots on the frill and toenails on the feet.

4. When the paint is dry, draw around the head with a thin black felt-tip pen. Add a face, then draw around the rest of the dinosaur.

5. Use a red pencil or chalk pastel to draw a curved line around the dinosaur's body. Draw more lines on the body, and on the tail and legs.

Chalk pastels make brighter patterns than pencils.

Try painting a pale blue patch under a dinosaur for a shadow.

More ideas

Try drawing party hats on your dinosaurs. Draw a cone on top of a dinosaur's head. Then, add short lines for a tassel at the top of the cone.

To add a squeaky blower in a dinosaur's mouth, draw a spiral, like this. Add little curved lines around it to show that it is moving.

You could draw a ribbon tied around a dinosaur's neck. Draw two loops for the bow and trailing ends for the rest of the ribbon.

Sparkly Christmas tree

Press hard
as you draw.

1. Using a light green wax crayon, draw a tree on white paper. Add a little trunk, a pot and a star. Then, draw a line for the floor beneath the tree.

The white crayon shapes are shown here in yellow so that you can see them.

2. Draw some presents under the tree. Then, use a white wax crayon to draw lots of stars around the tree. Add spots on the tree, too.

3. Mix lots of watery yellow paint, then brush it all over the paper. The wax crayon lines and shapes will resist the paint. Leave it to dry.

Paint some orange presents, too.

4. Brush watery pink paint on the tree, the presents and the floor. While it is still wet, dab yellow and orange paint on the tree. Fill in the star, too.

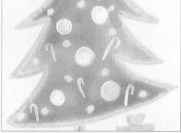

5. When the paint is dry, draw large round decorations with thick white paint or correction fluid. Add candy canes, too. Then, leave them all to dry.

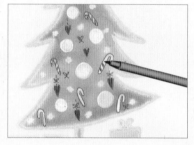

6. Draw some hearts with a red pencil. Using a red felt-tip pen, draw bows on some of the decorations. Add stripes on the candy canes, too.

7. Brush white glue on the big white decorations and sprinkle them with glitter. Dab dots of glue onto the star and sprinkle it with glitter, too.

8. Draw around the decorations with a bright pink pencil. Add a shape for hanging above each one, and fill it in with a paler pink pencil.

9. To make the tree even more sparkly, blob little dots of white glue onto the tree. Press a sparkly sequin or a bead onto each blob of glue.

To make this effect, brush some gold paint around the star.

You could also draw star decorations with a silver pen or glitter glue.

Tractor race collage

You don't need this blue circle.

1. For a tractor, draw a rectangle on a piece of red paper. Add a curve across the top right-hand corner. Then, cut out the shape, like this.

2. Glue the tractor onto a piece of white paper. Then, draw one big wheel and one smaller one on black paper. Cut out both wheels.

3. Draw around the big wheel on blue paper. Add a mudguard and two exhaust pipes. Cut out and glue on the mudguard and the pipes.

To make a big race, glue lots of tractors onto a large piece of paper.

You could draw a group of animals driving a tractor.

This piece of green paper was glued on for grass, before the tractors were glued on.

Look at the other tractors in the race for ideas of things to draw.

Try making a tractor with a long arm, like this one.

Your tractor could have a trailer with baby animals riding in it.

Draw spirals for the sheep's wool.

Add a stand for the seat.

4. Draw a seat and two round hubcaps on red paper. Draw a headlight on yellow paper, too. Then, cut out all the shapes and glue them on.

5. Using a pencil, draw a sheep driving. Add a steering wheel, then go over the lines with a thin black felt-tip pen. Fill in the sheep with pens.

6. Draw a radiator grill, vents and rivets on the tractor. Add bolts on the hubcaps and curling lines for steam. Then, add other tractors in the race.

Sugar Plum Fairy

Leave space at the top of the paper for the arms and wand.

1. To draw a Sugar Plum Fairy, draw a head on thick white paper. Add a neck and a bodice. Then, draw an oval for the bottom layer of the skirt.

2. Draw hair on the head, then add a face. Draw two curving arms, and a wand. Add two legs, overlapping the skirt a little. Then, draw the wings.

3. Mix some watery pink paint and brush it all over the ballerina. The pencil lines should still show through the paint. Then, leave it to dry.

Paint her wand, too.

4. Mix thick paint for the ballerina's skin. Fill in her face, arms and the top of her body. Use other thick paints to fill in her eyes, legs, hair and wings.

5. Rip an oval of purple or pink tissue paper about the same size as the skirt. Glue it onto the paper so that it overlaps the tops of the legs, like this.

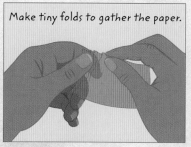

Make tiny folds to gather the paper.

6. Cut a strip of pink tissue paper for the top layer of the skirt. Gather it along one edge, then glue this edge along the ballerina's waist.

7. Cut a small bodice from pink paper. Cut a 'V' shape into the top. Then, glue the bodice on so that it overlaps the gathered edge of the skirt.

8. Draw over the ballerina's eyelashes, nose, cheeks and lips with pencils. Use felt-tip pens to draw ballet shoes and ribbons around her legs.

9. Brush glue on the wand and add a band across her waist. Sprinkle them both with glitter. When the glue is dry, shake off any extra glitter.

The Sugar Plum Fairy appears in a ballet called The Nutcracker. She lives in the Land of Sweets.

The Sugar Plum Fairy ballerina in this picture was cut out and glued onto a painted stage.

You could paint sweets to go around your ballerina.

Snowflake doodles

Look at the patterns on these snowflakes for ideas to doodle.

1. Use a blue pencil to draw four lines that cross each other in the middle. Then, add four more lines between them with a blue ballpoint pen.

2. Draw a circle in the middle of the snowflake with the pen, then fill it in. Add a little circle at the end of each line with the blue pencil.

3. Draw small leaf-shaped patterns along all of the pencil lines. You may find it easier if you turn your paper as you draw them.

Snowman in the snow

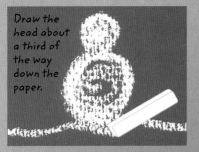

Draw the head about a third of the way down the paper.

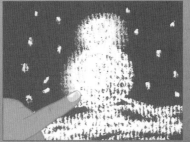

1. Using a white chalk, draw a circle on blue paper for the head. Fill it in, then add a larger circle below it. Draw a wavy line and fill in below it.

2. Draw chalk dots for snow around the snowman. Rub the edge of the snowman with a fingertip to smudge the chalk. Then, smudge the dots, too.

3. Lay scrap paper over the bottom of the picture so you don't smudge it any more. Use a black pencil to draw dots for eyes, a mouth and buttons.

4. Using a red pencil, draw a nose shaped like a carrot. Add a scarf around the neck. Then, fill them both in with red and orange stripes.

Tyrannosaurus rex

This painted background was added after the dinosaurs were finished.

1. Using a pencil, draw an oval for a dinosaur's head on white paper. Then, add a bigger oval for its body. Draw it below the head, at an angle.

2. For the neck, draw two curved lines joining the head and the body. Then, draw a tail with a pointed end, curving out behind the body.

For a dinosaur bending down, draw the ovals for its head and body in a straight line.

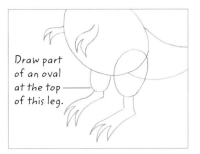

Draw part of an oval at the top of this leg.

The wax crayon will resist the paint.

3. Add short arms with claws near the top of the body. Draw ovals for the top part of the legs. Draw the lower part of the legs and add claws.

4. Use a white wax crayon to draw teeth. Add spots on the head, body and leg. They are all shown here in yellow so that you can see them.

5. Mix some watery purple paint. Fill in the dinosaur, but leave the tummy bare. Fill it in with watery green paint. Then, paint purple arms.

6. Leave the paint to dry. Then, draw a line along the top of the teeth with a purple pencil. Draw around the arms and the rest of the body.

7. Draw a purple zigzag along the bottom of the teeth. Then, draw a curved line, with a dot below it, for the eye. Add a dot and a line for a nostril.

This background was painted with watery paints. The mermaids were cut out and glued on when the paint had dried.

The pearl that this mermaid is holding was drawn with a wax crayon, then painted.

Try drawing mermaids with their arms and tails in different positions.

Swimming mermaids

Press lightly with a pencil.

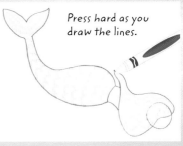

Press hard as you draw the lines.

1. Draw a circle for a mermaid's head near the bottom of a piece of white paper. Then, draw a big wavy shape overlapping the head, for hair.

2. Add two short curved lines for the mermaid's body, coming from the back of the hair. Then, draw a tail curving up from the body, like this.

3. Use a white wax crayon to draw scales on the tail and wavy lines on the hair. They are shown here in yellow so that you can see them.

The crayon lines will resist the paint.

4. Mix some runny paint for the mermaid's skin. Using a thin paintbrush, fill in her face and body. Then, add two arms stretching out in front of her.

5. Mix some watery purple paint. Then, fill in the mermaid's tail. Mix some watery orange paint then fill in the hair, too.

You could also paint shells and fish, and glue them onto your picture.

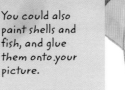

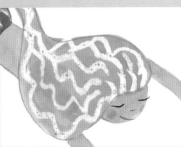

6. When the paint is dry, use felt-tip pens to draw the mermaid's face. Draw curved lines for eyes, a little nose, and a curved mouth.

To make the effect below, dab darker blue paint onto wet blue paint.

Tall giraffes

You could draw an insect flying around your giraffe.

Start drawing near the top of a piece of white paper.

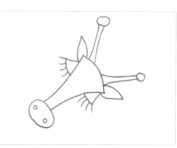

1. Using a pencil, draw an oval for a giraffe's nose. Add two curved lines coming up from it. Then, draw a curve for the top of the head.

2. Draw two ears, then add two triangles below them, for the eyes. Add eyelashes and nostrils. Then, draw horns on top of the giraffe's head.

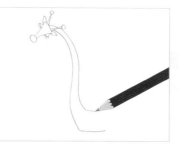

3. Draw one long curve and one slightly shorter curve for the giraffe's neck. Add a line for the tummy. Then, draw the rest of the body, too.

4. Add four long legs below the body. Make them narrow at the top and a little wider at the bottom, like this. Then, draw a tail sticking up.

The wax crayon will resist the paint.

5. Use a pale orange wax crayon to draw circles all over the giraffe's body. Then, draw grass around the feet with a green wax crayon.

6. Fill in the giraffe and the grass with watery paints. Then, when the paint is dry, draw over the pencil lines with a thin black pen.

For a giraffe stretching up to eat leaves, draw its head upside down, like this.

You could draw a giraffe with its neck bending down, too.

Fairy cake collage

Use the ideas in this picture for decorating your fairies and cakes.

Make each layer smaller than the one below it.

1. Cut a rectangle of tissue paper for the bottom layer of a cake. Glue it onto a piece of paper. Then, cut out more layers and glue them on, too.

2. Use a thin black felt-tip pen to draw around each layer. Decorate each layer with different patterns, such as circles, hearts and wavy lines.

Add gold hearts and spots, too.

3. Draw holders for candles on some of the layers. Then, cut candles from tissue paper and glue them on. Add flames with a gold felt-tip pen.

You could draw fairies doing different things, such as lighting a candle or carrying a cherry.

Try decorating a cake with tissue paper cherries.

Draw a wavy line along the bottom of the dress.

4. Cut a shape from tissue paper for a fairy's dress. Glue it near the cake. Then, cut out two pairs of wings and glue them next to the dress.

5. Use a thin black pen to draw around the dress and the wings. Draw the fairy's arms and legs. Then, add a neck and a curve for the head.

6. Use a gold pen to draw the fairy's hair. Draw her face, and add a wand. Fill in the wand with the gold pen, then add patterns on the dress and legs.

Busy farmyard

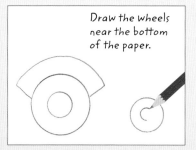

1. Pressing lightly, draw a big tractor wheel on a large piece of white paper. Add a hubcap and a mudguard. Then, draw a smaller wheel, too.

2. Starting at the top of the mudguard, draw a shape for the front of the tractor. Then, add an exhaust pipe and some grills, like this.

3. Draw a farmer sitting on the mudguard, holding a steering wheel. Draw the outline of his face, but don't draw his eye or mouth yet.

4. For chickens, draw small half-circle shapes. Add feathers at one end of each shape for a tail. Then, draw more feathers for wings.

5. Draw a pointed barn above the tractor. Add a roof, doors and a window. Then, draw a lock and lots of planks. Add a hedge and other animals.

6. Draw over all the pencil lines with felt-tip pens. Then, add curves on the wheels for treads. Draw circles on the hubcaps for bolts, too.

7. To fill in the tractor, dip a clean paintbrush into water. Brush in from the outlines, so that the ink runs. Then, fill in the other parts of the picture.

8. Leave the ink to dry. Then, draw the farmer's face with thin felt-tip pens. Draw details on the chickens and other animals, too.

9. For the background, fill in all the white spaces with watery brown paint. Leave a white border around each part of the picture, like this.

Add a painted
sun and sky.

You could draw a
lady farmer, too.

Draw curved
lines for smoke.

Dancing princesses

Use the ideas in this picture to draw princesses dancing in different positions.

Start drawing near the top of the paper.

1. Using a pencil, draw a rectangle for the bodice of a princess's dress on white paper. Add a neck above it, then draw her head.

2. Draw two curved lines for a parting in the hair, then add little curling lines at the ends of them. Draw long wavy hair flying out behind her, too.

3. Draw a little crown on top of the princess's head. Add a shape on either side of her neck, for a collar. Then, draw her eyes, nose and lips.

4. Draw one sleeve coming out to one side. Draw the other one coming down in front of her bodice. Then, draw the princess's hands.

You could decorate the paper around your princesses with little dots of paint.

Use very watery blue paint to paint a shadow under your dancing princess.

5. Draw a skirt with a curved bottom edge. Draw two little shoes, too. Then, add a sash around the waist, and a bow with long ribbons at the side.

6. Fill in the dress with watery paint. Mix paint for the skin, then paint the face, neck and hands. Paint the hair, crown, shoes and sash, too.

7. Decorate the dress, sash and bow with hearts and dots. When the paint is dry, draw over all the pencil lines with a thin black felt-tip pen.

Hungry sharks

Use a pencil.

1. Draw a long curve for the top of a shark's body on a piece of blue paper. Then, add two shorter curves at one end, for a smiling mouth.

2. Draw a curving line for the bottom of the body. Then, draw two curved triangles at the end of the body for the tail fin, like this.

Erase this line.

3. Draw a fin on top of the shark. Add a fin overlapping the underside of the body, too. Erase the line where the fin overlaps the body.

4. Draw over the pencil lines with a thin black pen. Add an eye and a nostril, then draw sharp teeth inside the mouth. Add gills on the body, too.

5. Mix some watery blue paint. Brush a line inside the shark's outline. Then, paint the sea around the shark with thicker dark blue paint.

6. When the paint is dry, use a white chalk or chalk pastel to fill in the middle of the body and fins. Smudge the chalk a little with your finger.

For a scene like this, draw lots of sharks on a large piece of paper. Paint the sharks and the sea, then add chalk details when everything is dry.

These little fish were drawn with chalk, then some were outlined using a black pen.

Draw three short lines for a closed eye.

You could draw a shark with its mouth closed.

93

Snowy trees

1. Use a blue felt-tip pen to draw a tree trunk on a piece of white paper. Add branches coming from the trunk. Draw little twigs on the branches.

Draw the tree trunks leaning at different angles.

2. Draw lots more trees, with large ones at the bottom of the paper and smaller ones at the top. The smaller trees will look as if they're far away.

Make the zigzags into a triangle.

3. Draw green zigzag trees in between the other trees. Add a short line for a trunk at the bottom. Then, fill any spaces with purple trees.

4. Use a white wax crayon to add lots of dots across the paper for snow. The dots are shown here in yellow so that you can see them.

5. Draw some hills above the trees with a pencil. Then, mix some watery blue paint. Fill in the hills and paint a shadow beneath each tree.

Paint a blue zigzag for a snowy road.

You could add animals in the snow between the trees, too.

6. When the paint is dry, mix some darker blue paint. Brush it across the sky, like this. Then, leave the painting to dry completely.

7. Dip a clean paintbrush into some water. Then, gently brush it around and around on top of a tree. The water will make the ink run.

8. Brush water over all the other blue trees. Then, rinse your brush well. Brush clean water over the green and purple trees in the same way.

Index

Photographs by Howard Allman • Photographic manipulation by John Russell and Nick Wakeford • Flowers on pages 40-41 © Digital Vision
First published in 2009 by Usborne Publishing Ltd., 83-85 Saffron Hill, London, EC1N 8RT, England www.usborne.com